inside

companion journal

inside

A Guide to the Resources Within

companion journal

An Intimate Self-Exploration

SARAH BRASSARD

Inside: A Guide to the Resources Within Companion Journal

© 2019 by Sarah Brassard

This book contains a variety of exercises that will stretch your physical body, your mind, your emotions, and your spirit. It is a multilayer process that involves identifying and revealing the injured, weakened aspects of your life and building a foundation that is strong enough to heal through them. The practices given in this book are not meant to take the place of the advice given to you by your primary care doctors. They are meant to be used as an adjunct to any current practices. When in doubt, be selective about the exercises you participate in, and call on the experts on your healing team for guidance.

Published 2019

ISBN: 978-0-9977127-5-9
Library of Congress Control Number: 2019916709

Cover and book design by Looker Lab 2019
Printed in the United States of America

www.SarahBrassard.com

CONTENTS

Introduction

Welcome home to your inner world!

This Companion Journal begins where *Inside* left off. It is my hope and prayer that this journal will call you inside even more and offer you an expression of yourself that you can chronicle and continue to cultivate.

I have been journaling most of my life and have volumes of books that have held my most intimate secrets until I have found the strength and confidence to bring them to the world. Writing is a fabulous first step in self-care. When we take the time to stop, reflect, and listen, we have an innermost view of what it is that makes us who we are, and that is priceless information.

The practices in this Companion Journal will help you receive, notice, and stay open to the many lessons pain and discomfort offer you when you have found strength enough to listen. That is the goal of self-care—to fortify your body, mind, heart, and spirit to meet the ever-changing experiences life delivers you. As you further develop your self-care practices, you will no longer push back from the lessons that appear, even the most difficult ones. You will find confidence and faith in the process and let go of the resistance of the goal-oriented mind and gracefully surrender to the journey of life.

The practices have been hand-picked to deepen your self-study and access your inner reserves, which will open self-awareness. This is the key to staying on a healing path, to continually learn about what makes you uniquely individual, and from that originality grow into the most beautiful expression of who you are.

I will offer you practices that will help you pay attention to your thoughts, notice your surroundings, and trust your intuition. How do you feel when you breathe, move, or have an unexpected memory rise to the surface? How do you feel in the many scenes of your life?

Through a dedicated practice of reflection and contemplation, you will find the courage to make the inner inquiry, and that will set you on a course of learning for the rest of your life.

Most of the practices take just minutes and can be done anywhere, in any order, or in direct response to a particular situation. Some require action, and others simply take place in the everyday moments of your life. Treasure your experience in the practice and journal how that experience made you feel from a physical, emotional, mental, and spiritual perspective. Each practice is created for you to remember who you are on the inside, under all that scares you, to awaken your inner knowledge and help you shift out of old habits that no longer work for you.

These are some examples:

- When an interaction leaves you feeling sad, confused, angry, anxious, or resentful, call on the **Grounding** practice. When we cultivate tools to take care of the feelings that show up, we build a powerful base that responds generously to the world around us.

- **Safe Haven** gives you a reference point for safety and security that you can call on and build on. When we have a sense of security, we have a valuable tool to move forward and meet the challenges ahead.

- Make an investigation into your personal happiness with **What Makes You Feel Joyful?** As we grow up and older, so many of us lose our connection to the joy we naturally experienced as a child. Sometimes the best way to know what makes us happiest is figuring out what doesn't make us happy.

- **Unwinding Your Body** is a simple, playful exercise that shows you how different it is to move from your spirit rather than your mind, and it has wonderful benefits for your overall system.

- **Finding Your Relationship to Trauma** allows us to gently revisit painful events, feel the impact of our experience, and work toward resolution of those events.

- **Self-Kindness** asks you to consider your voice as a powerful tool and to understand that everything you say has an impact on your life personally and exponentially. Your voice can be used to harm or to heal. How will you use your voice?

- **Awareness in Waking Up** quickly yet gently jump-starts your day with strength and purpose. Each day has so much potential; make the most of how you begin it.

- **A Beautiful Place to Rest** transforms our bedroom to a safe haven, a place to rest, rejuvenate, excite, and heal our lives. When we bring this kind of honor to our space, true healing happens.

It is not the intention of this book to tell you which spiritual quest is best suited for you but rather to help you build a base, a starting point, and ultimately a foundation strong enough to take you on the spiritual journey of your dreams.

You are the true teacher of your life, and each step you take on this self-care journey will bring you closer to your truth. Grow closer to yourself, believe in your ability to change, and watch the arms of your life warmly open to welcome you home once again. It is in this awakened state that you will live a purposeful and enlightened life.

chapter 1

Become the Explorer of Your Inner World

You'll understand that all the messages you are given, whether they come from physical discomfort, emotional upset, or spiritual crisis, have come to you for a reason. This is the language of your inner world.

Become the explorer of your inner world. Follow the intrigue of your inquiry to heal, and trust that you are on the path you need to be on, even if that path feels like the rockiest and steepest path of all. Wherever you are right now is exactly where you are supposed to be. It takes all sorts of circumstances to motivate us to look at life in a fresh and promising new way. So rather than judge the conditions of your life, bring awareness to them. Recognize the magnitude of your feelings and do your best to not get stuck there. As you will learn, the only way through discomfort and suffering is straight through it. Cherish the fact that you are feeling anything, even if those feelings are bringing you tremendous discomfort. It is better than the alternative of not feeling at all, and it is the first step on your path to healing.

Opening Yourself Up to Self-Healing

Self-healing means acting from a place of compassion for the body, mind, heart, and spirit. It is a gentle, nurturing relationship with your own needs that is a vital part of building a happy and fulfilled life.

Exercise: Self-healing opens a dialogue with the most precious parts of who you are inside. Describe your inner dialogue at this time, however it looks in your life (positive or negative).

_____

_____

_____

Self-care is a method of wellness that focuses on nurturing yourself so that you can be healthier in your body and mind, happier in your life, and a better loved one to those who care about you.

Exercise: Describe any self-care practices you have in your life now that support your health and happiness.

Practices

- -

GROUNDING

Grounding practices plant us firmly in the power of our life. In this practice, I ask you to notice yourself not as a victim of the circumstances around you but as a powerful contributor. Use this technique when a situation or interaction with someone leaves you feeling sad, confused, angry, anxious, or resentful.

1 Sit on a chair or in a comfy supported seat on the floor and breathe into your connection to the earth. Feel the energetic contact and imagine roots growing deeply into the earth from the base of your spine or feet. Breathe into these roots and visualize them going deep and wide into the ground. Spend as much time here as you need to in order to feel fully supported.

2 Ask yourself, "How did this situation make me feel?"

3 If there is negativity in your answer, rather than digging in further to what might be going on, simply offer yourself the chance to feel grounded and safe through your connection to the earth in this moment.

JOURNALING

The power of putting pen to paper is storied, and the how-to is simple: write it down. The most effective journaling is a mirror, a release valve, and a vision board. It's a medium without judgment because the only audience for your journal will be you. With a dedicated journaling practice you will be able to reflect on the changes that arise from the simple act of looking inside.

1. Being Grateful

First thing in the morning, open your journal and write down three things that you're grateful for. It can be anything you want it to be; it is for your eyes only. These are some examples of things I am grateful for in my life:

* My relationship with God, the universe, and nature

* Living close to a hiking trail

* Fresh air

- The seashore
- Comfy sheets and blankets
- Manicures/pedicures
- My garden
- Summer parties on the deck

2. Letting It Out

For this practice, simply make note of what's on your mind.

For example:

- "I keep getting distracted when my boss puts me on the spot."
- "I'm so fat. I can't say no to cheesecake."
- "I miss him/her. I'm so lonely."

The cleanest statements are the easiest to address. You may find that they are also the hardest to write. I encourage you to practice writing these sorts of statements:

- "I don't like the way he spoke to me."
- "I'd like to learn to cook better."
- "My father-in-law gets on my nerves."
- "The dog is out of control."

Or simply unwind. For example:

- "That made me so mad I couldn't see straight. Who does she think she is?"
- "I had to get out of there. I felt like the walls were closing in on me."
- "It was amazing, he made me feel like the only person in the room!"

As you do this exercise, you're not looking for profundity. You're looking for truth, your truth. Spend as much time as you need—keep writing until you've let it all out!

CREATE A VISION BOARD IN 5 STEPS

A vision board is where your thoughts become actions. First put your vision on paper. It can be about anything. Then build on what appears and continue to write about it. Dream big, indulge yourself in thoughts of love and growth, and visualize what it will feel like when your vision is realized. Be specific and positive here. Put it out there! I've added this vision board description from my website to further support your vision board experience.

1 Pick up magazines that draw you to them. Then start cutting out images, words, and headlines that make you smile. Gather all your materials before you start gluing.

2 Go through the images and lay out your favorites on the board. Take away any images that no longer feel right, and use your intuition to pin down the images, words, and headlines that feel the best. As you do this, you'll get a sense of how the board will take shape.

3 Start laying the images in a pattern that represents what you'd like to draw into your life. Begin gluing the images, words, headlines, and anything else that feels supportive of your vision. You can write and paint on it too—your vision board is yours to create and manifest.

4 This is optional, but a self-affirming step: Leave a space in the center of the board for a beautiful, happy picture of yourself.

5 Hang your board in your sacred space, bathroom, or anywhere you'll see it regularly. Bring your focus to it as often as possible and watch your dreams unfold.

chapter 2

Waking Up to Myself

We are all unique in how we respond to life's events. What hurts and harms one person may be a non-issue for someone else. We each have our individual sensitivities, and once we know what they are, we have the ability to know how to relate to them.

Waking up to ourselves is the greatest knowledge we can capture. You will find tools to help you heal what needs to be healed. You will no longer judge whether or not these feelings are worthy of healing. When they show up, they are there to be healed. It is this type of healing that encourages us to reawaken, to come out from under the protective walls that at one time may have helped us cope but no longer help us grow. Then you wake up and take part in your life once again.

Illumination

Exercise: Write down a life-changing event.

Example*: The events that made the biggest impression on my life happened long ago. Four decades back, my mother left our family and my father died shortly thereafter from complications of leukemia. These life-changing events left me with a traumatic imprint of loss and abandonment.*

_____

_____

_____

_____

_____

Reawakening My Inner Child

Exercise: Do you have a relationship with your inner child? Can you relate to what that might mean in your life?

Example: In the losses of my young life, my inner child, the person I was when I was born, went away. That tender, trusting, open child was no longer a part of who I was. I couldn't remember what it was like to have faith, to be spontaneous, and to be free from the burdens of fear. I had no relationship with my inner child.

_____

_____

_____

_____

_____

Release Blame, Accept Responsibility

Exercise: Are you holding others responsible for your state of well-being? Write about this.

What would it feel like to accept full responsibility for your life?

When challenges present, what do you do to self-soothe?

Example: One of the most challenging things for me to heal through was blame. In my most fragile times, I placed blame and responsibility for my difficulties on others and would fall victim to what was going on around me. When we take inventory of our lives, we become empowered. No one else holds any of our cards; we call all the shots in our healing.

_____

_____

_____

_____

_____

Practices

SAFE HAVEN

Fear puts a blanket over all that makes you feel safe and secure. This practice puts you back in relationship with that security and gives you the courage to take the next steps to heal.

1 Find a quiet place in your home. Sit on a chair or a supported seat on the floor. (If you are on a chair, make sure your feet can touch the ground.)

2 Lengthen your spine and take three deep breaths.

3 Visualize your breath coming in from the ground below you.

4 Feel yourself drink in the energy of the earth through your feet. (If you are on the ground, feel this same energy come through all parts of your body that touch the ground.)

5 Now close your eyes and visualize in your mind's eye a place that brings you comfort.

6 With your eyes closed, pay attention to the details of your safe haven. Allow this experience to be all yours. Let your imagination grow your safe haven's beauty, and blanket yourself in it.

Notice:

* The color of the sky, the temperature of the air
* How you feel physically, emotionally, mentally, and spiritually
* The vibrancy of the foliage around you.
    + Are there trees, plants, and flowers nearby?
    + What color are they?
    + Do they have a fragrance?
    + Are there birds, butterflies, dragonflies, or animals with you?
    + What else is there?

When you have established this place in your mind, you will be able to rely on it no matter where you are or what's going on around you. It will be there for you whenever you need it.

WHAT MAKES YOU FEEL JOYFUL?

Think of this practice as an investigation into happiness, and let what you write inform you about your connection with joy.

Make a list of words that evoke a feeling of joy. These are some of mine:

* Kindness
* Compassion
* Forgiveness
* Generosity
* Calmness
* Positivity
* Laughter
* Reflection
* Patience

Take each of the words you jotted down and write a couple of sentences on each of them, describing when you experience it most.

1 What activities are you doing when you feel these emotions?

2 How do you feel in your body when you are doing these activities?
   + What is the quality of your breath?
   + Is your mind clear and focused?
   + Do you have a feeling of safety?

3 How could you bring more of this activity into your life and feel supported by the happiness it brings you?

Let your imagination flourish. Build on what makes you feel best when times are tough. You could transform a room to hold your treasures—photos of loved ones, flowers, and your meditation space—or it can be an activity like taking a walk on a favorite trail or taking your dog to the dog park to see familiar, friendly faces.

This is a valuable tool, one that you can call on as a loyal friend to help lift your spirits in difficult times. It will encourage you to keep going when you want to throw your arms in the air and give up, and it will help you build an infrastructure for deep healing.

VALIDATION

Validating loss will support you in letting go of the story and allow you to take the next steps in healing. Give yourself permission to know the impact of your trauma so you can get on with your life. Trauma in your life may involve a variety of factors. For this practice, I address the most pressing feelings at this moment. These emotions might be connected with what happened long ago or what is happening right now in your life. It doesn't really matter what the details are. Stand witness to your feelings without judgment—hear them, experience them, and validate them—so you can release them.

1 Find a place in your home or office where you can be alone and undisturbed.

2 Make it a place where you feel very safe. Bring a journal, a pen, a timer, tissues, and anything else that helps you feel supported.

3 Set your timer for three to six minutes. You may want to start with three minutes and work up to six minutes depending on how you feel going into the practice. As always, honor where you are before you start.

4 Without lifting your pen, write the first things that come to your mind when you ask these three questions:

   + What did this event take from my life?
   + What injustices did this event impose on my life?
   + What would my life be like had this not happened?

When you have completed your journaling for the day, take the sheets of paper and find a place where you can safely burn the contents, such as a fireplace or an outdoor fire pit. As you ceremonially light the paper, ask, "Do I need to revisit this again tomorrow?" If yes, make time to do this exercise again the next day. Ask this question every time you do this ritual until you feel the story let go of you.

After your burning ceremony is complete, take a comfortable seat and read the intention below or an intention of your own that you have created. Complete the ceremony with gratitude for the experience.

INTENTION

I have suffered the effects of:

_____

_____

_____

_____

(fill in the event that has brought you suffering). I have felt the sadness it has brought to my life. Thank you for bringing to light the parts of me that call for healing. I am grateful, and now I am ready to release the hurt and anger and move on.

chapter 3

Trauma Comes in All Shapes and Forms

There are two different forms of trauma: hard trauma and soft trauma. Hard trauma is recognized as having an identifiable beginning and end that is shocking and outside the norm of human experience, such as violent death, natural disasters, personal assaults, and wartime tragedies. Soft trauma is not as easily identifiable or understood. It can show up as long-time abuse, neglect by someone we depend on, or the unresolved sorrow, anger, and resentment in our lives.

Many of us don't recognize that trauma exists in our lives; what we do know is that life hurts and we want it to feel differently. There's a cloud that hangs over us that we can never quite shake. We get used to the discouraging situations and instead of investigating the root of the sadness, we find ways to live with it. Our systems—physical, emotional, mental, and spiritual—are highly sensitive and incredibly powerful. When we recognize trauma in our life and take steps to heal through it, miracles happen that you never imagined possible.

Identifying Trauma in Your Life

The truth is that trauma comes in all shapes and forms, just like we do. What does seem to be universal is that trauma can be defined as an event that once experienced leaves an imprint on your life that affects everything you do moving forward.

Exercise: How has trauma presented in your life? Write down what comes up.

Can you identify whether your trauma was hard trauma or ongoing soft trauma, or a combination?

_____

_____

_____

_____

_____

_____

Healing through Trauma Is a Heroic Act

One of my favorite authors and greatest teachers, Joseph Campbell, describes the process of healing through trauma as the hero's journey. Campbell says that the hero is "a person that has found a supernormal range of human and spiritual life and then comes back to communicate it . . . it's a cycle." When we find the strength to slay the inner dragon of the mind and ego through self-love, we have the opportunity to become the hero in our own lives.

To slay the inner dragon (your trauma) you must adopt a dedicated practice of self-care. What does that look like in your life and is it enough to keep you on a path of healing?

_____

_____

_____

_____

_____

_____

_____

Practices

‑‑‑ ‑‑ ‑‑‑

UNWINDING YOUR BODY

Here's an easy way of judging if you need to unwind: Stand tall, balancing equally on both feet. Close your eyes and notice how your body moves. If you feel yourself moving in small circles or side to side, your body would benefit from this release. This simple, playful exercise shows you how different it is to move from your spirit instead of your mind, and it has wonderful benefits for the overall system.

1 Find a room with a clean area where you can be on the floor and roll around.

2 Imagine your energy has gotten all bound up, like a chord or a rope that needs unraveling.

3 Set an intention, such as: *I am going to unwind and release the bound-up energy in my body.*

4 Allow yourself to roll around in a way that is instructed by your spirit rather than your mind, and let go. It may feel a bit contorted at times, but do your best to go with it (always staying safe in the process).

5 When you have had enough, simply say, *I am done unwinding*. Lie down for a few minutes and allow the experience to sink in and heal you at a very deep level.

FINDING YOUR RELATIONSHIP TO TRAUMA

It is very hard to revisit events that have caused us pain. But when we find the strength to go back and really feel the impact of our experience, we have more of a chance of resolving the inner pain and the disturbances that pain creates in our lives when unresolved.

Find a quiet place that feels safe, then ask yourself the questions below. But before you set out, understand that what appears could bring up difficult emotions like judgment, shame, or embarrassment. If so, relate to these emotions as words only and avoid feeding into a storyline that takes your attention from the practice before you. Open your heart to whatever shows up. When you turn the mirror toward yourself, you have all the power needed to change anything and everything in your life. This is your chance to reset old habits and pave the way for new, revitalizing ways of being to take form.

Be sure to write down your questions and answers in your journal so you can reread them and feel how you resonate in your body, mind, and spirit. This is just the beginning of understanding what you feel inside, and these questions are just some examples of what to ask. Feel free to build on these questions, get as creative as you like, and tailor your line of questioning to the events specific to your life.

1 Are you easily overwhelmed?

2 Does stress overwhelm you?

3 Do you load one enormous event on top of another?

4 Do you take your time to assess the situation in front of you before you act out?

5 Do you make good decisions under pressure?

6 Do you regret your actions or second-guess yourself often?

chapter 4

Putting a Plan for Self-Healing in Place

The creative spirit knows no boundaries. It is expansive, infinite, and ranges out there beyond the restrictive walls of the mind and thought. It is transcendent, and our heroic life's quest is to find the strength to move toward those infinite boundaries.

Healing doesn't work with a measured type of progress. This is an adventure that you will be on for the rest of your life. Once you have that understanding, you can let go of the pressure to succeed and stay open to what appears going forward in your life. You are gathering the provisions you need to make that journey inward. Each step you take in that direction will enable you to look at your greatest dreams and move toward them. The only thing separating any of us from our greatest dreams is our fear. Take the pressure off and start to have fun. Be curious, open, and forgiving of yourself as you learn, and know that in that place everything is possible.

Preparing the Way for Self Healing

The key to staying on the path is knowing your truth, having an awareness of where you are, and sticking with a self-discipline that holds you steady on a path of self-healing. Being aware of your energy means that you replenish your strength before you've even noticed that you are starting to grow weak. Self-care is easiest when you have a structure in place to sustain it.

Exercise: Write down what an infrastructure of self-care would look like in your life. If a practice already exists in your life, write about it.

_____

_____

_____

_____

_____

_____

Create a Place of Rest Inside Yourself

All paths lead home when we prioritize the love of self first. You have come this far. The hardest work is done because you have decided to look deeper than the symptoms of your life. For those of us who have lived in pain, reconnecting to that peaceful place inside becomes the mission of our lives.

Exercise: Do you have a peaceful place inside? What is it? If you don't have one, how would you go about establishing one?

_____

_____

_____

_____

_____

_____

Practice

FINDING A SAFE PLACE WITHIN

When we build a relationship with safety and security and have established a place for our hearts to rest, we are not afraid to experience life's disruptions. We observe how challenges help us grow and learn.

1 Imagine a place anywhere in the world that represents safety to you. Make it a place in your mind that feels tremendously safe. In your mind's eye, build it out in a way that you are able to see, feel, and hear it. See the light. Listen to the sounds. Take in the smells. Notice how your environment feels on your skin. Use your breath to get there. Feel the comfort that this place invokes in you.

2 Spend time in your safe place and know that you can access its safety at any time and from anywhere. This is the place you'll rest your heart.

3 Let your creative mind go. Then go to this place anytime you feel unsafe, be it on a physical, emotional, mental, or spiritual level.

4 Do this practice as often as you can today, and keep building on it throughout the week. Journal about anything that comes up that you might find useful.

chapter 5

Growing Your Beginner's Mind

The beginner's mind reminds us of how much there is to learn—and what good news that is. There is nothing to prove and everything to gain. Letting go of the old, worn out information that no longer feels like it's adding quality to your life is a great place to start.

How would it feel to unload the burden of *knowing all the things you need to know* about your life and landing in a place that is open and curious about what's ahead? When fear, anxiety, and other negative feelings overwhelm you, there is literally no space in your life to take in more information. This is the great value of arriving in the beginner's mind. You are a wide-open vessel ready to fill up on new ways of being. Every day and every moment is different. The beginner's mind ushers in all possibilities for a fresh start.

What is Growing a Beginner's Mind?

When you embrace yourself as a beginner, there are no restrictions on what can happen. You have the wonder and curiosity of someone starting anew. Children embody the beginner's mind: living in the moment without expectation, not because they are trying to, but because they naturally act that way without the mind's interference. The more we can learn from their example, the better chance we have at living in the moment too.

Exercise: What does growing a beginner's mind mean to you? Are you curious about this opportunity or does it feel daunting and scary?

_____

_____

_____

_____

_____

Nurture Yourself as a Child

Think of the wounded parts of you as your child within.

Exercise: What would you do to take care of that inner child if life got frightening for her?

_____

_____

_____

_____

_____

_____

Practices

- -

SELF KINDNESS

In this practice, I ask you to consider your voice as a powerful tool. Understand that everything you say has an impact on your life personally and exponentially. Your voice can be used to harm or heal. How will you use your voice?

Part 1

1 Only say positive things to yourself and others today. When you speak, notice the quality and intention of what you are saying and ask yourself how it serves you and those around you.

2 Use kind words or stay quiet.

3 Watch people as you speak kindly to them; notice their body language and how grateful they are, and then notice how this makes you feel inside.

Part 2

1 Look in the mirror and give yourself a compliment. Look at your eyes—notice the color, the shape, and the expression they hold.

2 If you look tired or sad, bless yourself with hope and encouragement.

3 Close your eyes and visualize the healthiest, happiest version of yourself. Feel gratitude as you inhale and wash yourself in gratitude, and on the exhale release any negativity this exercise brings up for you.

4 Finish with "I love you."

MORNING REFLECTION

This practice is a gentle introduction to meditation. It does not take on the structure of a sitting practice but helps you release the urgency of jumping out of bed before taking time to reflect. It will give you an understanding of how important it is to pause before losing yourself in any activity. It will connect you with the vital systems of your life, your breath, your heartbeat, and the energy of your naval center. Don't underestimate the potency of this simple practice! Devote yourself to it and journal your discoveries. You'll be amazed at how much you'll learn.

1 In the morning before you get out of bed, lay still and place your right hand on your heart and your left hand on your belly. Breathe deeply, filling your lungs and expanding your torso as you inhale and pulling your navel back to your spine as you exhale, emptying your lungs. Notice your breath. Does it flow easily? Is there any restriction? If so, where in the body do you feel the restriction? How does taking this time feel to you? What ideas float into your head as you breathe? What emotions fill you? Practice this for six rounds of breath (an inhale and an exhale counts as one round) before you get out of bed.

2 Swing your legs over the bed, letting your feet either dangle or rest on the ground. Pay attention to the lengthening of your spine. It is important to have a strong, lengthened spine to support the energy in your body so you can feel the healing benefits of this breathing exercise.

3 Visualize a place that makes you feel safe, centered, and grounded. Bring three more rounds of breath to that feeling of safety. You may visualize what that place looks like, or it might just be a feeling. Whatever it is, fully experience what shows up. Close your eyes, place your hands on your heart, and give gratitude to yourself for making time in your day to do this practice.

Practice this every day for a week and notice the difference it makes in your life. Note the benefits and the struggles you encounter in your journal. If you feel ready for it, keep going with the practices beyond the week, with the ultimate goal of completing the practice every morning for forty days in a row.

chapter 6

Cultivating the Witness in You

From the foundation of gentle self-care we can now move to some of the more advanced elements of this journey.

Cultivating the witness means cultivating awareness. Observing how you think, what you say, and how you react to the circumstances of life. Becoming the observer diffuses the anxiety in any situation and helps you respond in a way that makes you feel safe and strong. When you step away from highly charged emotional experiences, just for a moment, shifts of awareness happen. These shifts allow you to be more generous in your actions. You begin to see your thoughts through a different lens, a more compassionate one that nurtures nonjudgment and allows you to be accountable. From there, you respond to life in a thoughtful and deliberate manner.

Detecting the Storm Inside You

When panic is triggered, adrenaline rushes into your body, alerts your mind, and has you reacting to an event, consciously or subconsciously, in one way or another. Sometimes these events are worthy of immediate reaction, but oftentimes they are not. It only takes a millisecond of an anxiety response to throw the world into a tailspin.

Exercise: Have you felt the storm inside you? Do you remember a time when you overreacted to a situation and felt regret afterward? Write about your experience.

_____

_____

_____

_____

_____

_____

Becoming the Observer

Unlike the weather outside, we can stand back and decide whether we'll become the storm or be the observer of the storm.

Exercise: After an emotional storm, is it your tendency to pick up the pieces by blaming others for your anger? Or do you take complete responsibility for your actions?

_____

_____

_____

_____

_____

_____

Practices

SEEING LIFE THROUGH THE OBSERVERS LENS

Does the awareness of the storm and the observer make you feel unsettled? Does it ignite a storm in you, or are you comfortable with this understanding? Whatever the case may be, just asking the question directs your attention inward, and that is the purpose of every practice. With this practice you'll ease into the experience of being the observer and notice life from a spacious perspective.

At the beginning of the day, identify situations that might allow you to step back and observe what is going on in a different way. You do not have to physically step back; just try to observe and listen with a new level of awareness.

In your moments of quiet reflection, begin viewing your life as though you were watching it on a movie screen. Instead of responding to what you see, hear, and feel with judgment, be in the moment with what is before you. Notice the details of what's going on and allow the information to flow through your senses instead of getting tangled in opinions about what appears. Be curious.

When the "movie" is over, do you like what you have seen? How could you best support the situation? Take time to journal your feelings about what appeared and how it felt to look at life in this way. How did it feel to let the events flow through you instead of analyzing and having an opinion on everything that happened? What surprised you or provoked some other emotional reaction?

When you see your life through the lens of the observer, you start to feel like you are in partnership with the universe. That is the truth of our lives. We are never alone, but anxiety, fear, and suffering can absolutely make us feel that way. So now instead of fending off what life brings to you, how about turning toward that ever-present energy and recognizing that you are the common denominator in all the events of your life?

STOP, LOOK, AND LISTEN

I have worked with the concept of the observer for most of my career, and I have found one of the most effective techniques to grasp it is something I call Stop, Look, and Listen. This practice will help you call on the observer and teach you to pause before addressing any alarming circumstances.

1 **Stop**. When the observer in you recognizes that something is triggering you, it's time to hit the pause button. Take the power of the moment back for yourself. Sometimes this means literally excusing yourself from a situation, stepping into the bathroom, getting off the phone. You will learn respectful ways of doing this. Be kind in your actions and you will discover how easily you can move through discomfort when it appears. Be alone and still for a moment. Experience what has appeared and take a long deep breath to help you feel space.

2 **Look**. Take a fresh look at the situation from other perspectives, beyond just your own gut reaction. This can be the most difficult part of the practice. We have been reacting to trigger situations the same way for a very long time, so the brain will instinctively want to go back to that reactive state. Stand strong and guide yourself toward the view of the observer. Observing deeply before reacting guides the brain in another direction. It sends the message that you are choosing a calmer way of dealing with the situation. The trigger itself matters less than your awareness. Look at everything—the physical, emotional, mental, and spiritual—from the triggered state. Deeply feel what this experience has brought up for you. Do your best, and take as much time as you need before moving on.

3 **Listen**. This is the part of the exercise that cultivates your relationship with the observer. You ask yourself, "What do I do next?" This is the opportunity to trust what comes through and know that it comes from a far more compassionate and generous place than what the ego would offer. How you proceed now will change your experience. When you see changes in your actions, you will feel encouraged and motivated to keep up. Soon you will find yourself guided more instinctively to this way of coping.

chapter 7

Making Space for the Sacred

You are sacred. This is a powerful statement, and each of us will react to it in a different way when we say it. You might be ready to believe these words. If you feel hesitation, though, you're not alone. When we struggle with emotions like anxiety, sadness, fear, and resentment, we can feel anything but sacred. Hard times and sorrow can beat us down, cover up our connection with the sacred within, dim the light, or silence its wisdom completely, but it is still there.

When we think of the word *sacred*, words like *holy, blessed*, and *revered* come to mind. We associate these words with religious acts, saints, and gurus—but not necessarily ourselves. What if we included ourselves in this level of honoring? How different would life feel if you were to share the sacred inside you on a daily basis? What would that look and feel like? Close your eyes, wherever you are right now, and say out loud: "I am sacred, I am sacred, I am sacred." Each time you recite those words, you get a big dose of self-love. Let me guide you back to that place inside you that is sacred. Let's lift the veil that separates you from your sacredness and tap into the part of you that already knows this to be true.

Letting the Sacred In

Exercise: Think of an experience and emotion that pulled you from honoring yourself as sacred.

_____

_____

_____

_____

Your Sacred Space and Daily Rituals

When you bring your energy to your sacred space, you take a seat with yourself and your highest source. You honor the importance of taking time to be with your life. You take time to create a place that holds you. This in itself is a potent meditation. Think of this place as your temple, a place you take your heart to feel safe, a place that you can always go to when life feels challenging.

Exercise: Do you have a physical space in your life now that inspires security and comfort? If so, describe it. If not, how do you feel about creating sacred space?

_____

_____

_____

_____

_____

_____

Practices

CREATE YOUR SACRED SPACE

There are no rules for the creation of altars or sacred space. Just think of it as a practice of creative expression that pays tribute to your unique inner self. Have fun with this exercise: tap into your primal inner resources and allow whatever makes your heart happy to run wild.

1 **Pick a spot that's private and won't get disturbed**. Ideally this is a corner that belongs to you alone. Give thought to how much room you'll need to stretch out your body, especially if you are going to do yoga or other exercises in the space. Your spot should have gentle light. Consider the direction that your space faces and the view. Seek a space that is as quiet as possible. Above all, it should be welcoming for you. The more you come to that special place, the more familiar you will be with it and the more you will be energetically called back to it.

2 **Make your area comfortable**. Dust and wipe down the surfaces to give your space a feeling of freshness. You can energetically clean the space by setting down a bowl of salt water to absorb and transform negativity or other disturbances, or you can burn sage or incense, or do both. The most important part of your sacred space is a comfortable place to sit so your body can feel settled and quiet and the agitation of your mind is soothed. In Kundalini yoga, we use a sheepskin, but a folded natural fiber blanket will also work beautifully. Feel free to use a meditation stool, a chair, or stacks of pillows. You decide what suits you best. Remember that you are the one steering the ship, so it's up to you to figure out what best suits you.

3 **Adorn your space**. Add a shelf or small table and make a display of things that hold meaning for you: photographs, artwork, prayer cards, jewelry, candles, incense, natural objects, books, and so on. Some people like to bring a "treasure box," a small, ornate container filled with meaningful objects, to their sacred space. Whatever you do to adorn your space, do it with intention and awareness.

4 **Bring your journal and a pen**. So much thoughtful work will take place here that you might want to make notes in your journal. A box of tissues may also be useful, as may a meditation timer or small clock.

5 **For those of you on the go, condense the essentials to their most portable form**. Take your mat and blanket or sheepskin with you in a tote. Find a special pouch to carry your sacred items in. Bring a sense of continuity and familiarity to your experience by stimulating your senses the same way every time, no matter where you are: feel the same blanket under you, smell the same incense or oil, hear the same timekeeper, and see the same candles or cards.

You are building your practice from the bottom up. Your sacred space will help you remember and honor the commitment you have made to yourself. This space is your temple, your place of worship. Be mindful and generous in creating it.

MEETING THE FOUR ELEMENTS: BODY, MIND, HEART, AND SPIRIT

The object of this practice is to learn a different way of relating to yourself in which your body, mind, heart, and spirit begin to feel familiar and safe to you. To do so, rather than looking at yourself from the outside in, you'll start to relate to yourself from the inside out. From there you'll bring your attention to each of the Four Elements.

1 Find a quiet, private place, sit down, and get comfortable. Have a piece of paper or a journal and pen available.

2 Take a deep breath in and out. Then inhale awareness, exhale judgment.

3 Say out loud or in your mind (whichever feels more comfortable), "I am open to experiencing myself from the inside out."

4 Take another deep breath. Say the name of the First Element: "Body." Take a deep breath. Repeat a second and third time.

5 Say the name of the Second Element: "Mind." Take a deep breath. Repeat a second and third time.

6 Say the name of the Third Element: "Heart." Take a deep breath. Repeat a second and third time.

7 Say the name of the Fourth Element: "Spirit." Take a deep breath. Repeat a second and third time.

8 Ask your body how it feels. Sit quietly and open yourself up to an answer. Write down anything important that comes to you. Do your best not to judge or reason away any answer that appears. Trust the first feelings that come to you.

9 Repeat by asking your mind how it feels.

10 Repeat again by asking your heart how it feels.

11 Repeat once more by asking your spirit how it feels.

12 Close the practice by thanking the messages that appeared.

chapter 8

The Body

Of the Four Elements the body is our most solid foundation. With a healthy body, great strides of healing can be made in the heart, mind, and spirit. Listening, learning, and honoring the body's messages is a beautiful way of opening up to all sorts of healing opportunities.

Your body is the temple of your life, the sacred place where you live. When you honor the body, the body speaks to you constantly. You are able to assess how stress affects you and do something about it. You know when you are tired and need to rest and refuel. You don't need to wait until you catch the flu, get foggy from lack of sleep, or feel overcome with anxiety or depression. Creating a deep awareness of the body clues you in to the telltale signs of depletion before major problems interrupt daily life. As you learn to listen to the sacred information that the body urges you to hear, you can respond lovingly with gentle self-care.

The Body Is Life's Vehicle

The body carries us through life. Without this means of transportation, we have little ability to make much happen. Let this simple knowledge inspire you to take ultimate care of your precious vehicle.

Exercise: How would your body feel if you consistently ate nourishing whole foods, exercised daily, alleviated every moment of stress with self-care techniques, and cultivated a way of life that had laughter, purpose, and meaning in it? What would be different? What would your life look like?

_____

_____

The Healing Breath

My whole perspective changed the day I joined a yoga class and learned that there were healthy and unhealthy ways to breathe. After learning how to breathe in the most efficient way, the yogic way, I was astonished at how powerful a healer the breath could be. The effects of yogic breath have enormous benefits to our physical being, heart, mind, and spirit.

Exercise: Place your hands on your belly and take a deep inhale. Does your belly expand or contract? How does it feel?

_____

_____

_____

_____

_____

_____

Practices

- - -   - - -

THE LONG DEEP BREATH

This simple practice will give you knowledge about how you are breathing and help you understand the subtleties of breath. As you become familiar with this breathing technique, you will have the chance to use it in the many situations of your life.

1 Sit in a chair or on the ground in a position that allows your spine the ability to lengthen. Use whatever pillows or props you need to make this position as comfortable as possible.

2 Sit tall and feel the crown of your head reaching toward the sky.

3 Tip your chin just enough to lengthen the back of your neck, so your breath can flow freely.

4 Place your hands on your belly and breathe as you normally breathe. Notice: Is your belly pulling in when you take a breath, or is it pushing out? If your belly pulls in on the inhale, your breath will be shallow, with the air entering only the upper part of your lungs. When your body expands with the inhale, your lungs inflate like a balloon and are filled with fresh air. This is the correct way to practice the Long Deep Breath.

5 Keep your hands on your belly as you practice. Inhale. Feel your chest lift and your belly and ribs expand. If your breath doesn't make it to your belly at first, don't worry. Allow it to go where it feels most natural, and over the course of time, work toward moving it deeper and deeper into your body. With practice and dedication, it will happen.

6 Exhale. Feel your belly and ribs release and deflate, first from your belly and up to your chest. Let all the air from your lungs go.

7 Start again.

8 Repeat the breath for three minutes.

Do this simple practice once a day for forty days to reap its life-altering benefits. You can also bring the Long Deep Breath into any situation either sitting or standing even for a few seconds or a minute when an element of calming and equanimity is called for.

ALTERNATE NOSTRIL BREATHING

Alternate Nostril Breathing brings awareness to the flow of air that moves through each of our nostrils at any given time. This may seem insignificant, but it actually is very important. Breathing through each nostril brings a different benefit. The left nostril encourages relaxation and calm, the right nostril energizes our overall system, and alternate nostril breathing is helpful in balancing the two hemispheres of the brain, improving sleep, bringing on clarity of thinking, and returning overall balance to the body. Alternate nostril breathing is a beautiful preparation for meditation.

1 Sit cross-legged or in a chair or stand in a comfortable position.

2 Relax your left arm and rest your left hand in your lap with the palm facing up.

3 Lift your right arm and press your right thumb against your right nostril. Your right nostril should be closed off but not in a way that's uncomfortable.

4 Inhale slowly through your left nostril.

5 When the inhale is complete, close off your left nostril with your pointer finger and exhale through your right nostril.

6 Inhale through your right nostril, change finger position, and exhale through your left nostril.

7 Repeat the motions above for three to six minutes of breathing.

8 Close the practice by releasing both nostrils and taking a deep breath in. Hold the breath for a count of ten, then exhale slowly.

chapter 9

The Mind

The mind is the initiator of action in life, and can be one of the greatest allies we have. In order to keep it in good health, we must understand what balance looks like in the mind and, equally, what imbalance looks like. The mind becomes gentler and more efficient when we have tools in place to make adjustments when needed.

To take good care of our minds we turn to our old friend the observer. Notice what your mind is doing right now. Is it present to the information in front of you? Or is it off on another task completely? As you have learned, noticing is a beautiful first healing step and a wonderful way to stimulate the brain and the mind, and it can be a portal to the health, balance, and well-being of the mind.

Making Meditation Work for You

In the daily ritual of meditation, we listen deeply to what our observations reveal to us. We slow everything down by dropping into a space and time that is devoted just to us. For right now, just imagine how sweet it is to spend time with someone you love and how wonderful it feels to have time to listen to their feelings. How about if that loved one was you. You are worth this time. You are worth this effort. Meditation can help you create this. This is a chance to quiet the noise of the outside world, spend time looking inward, and build an energetic foundation that holds whatever your life experience reveals.

Exercise: Meditation is a game changer, but feeling resistance to going inward is a very real obstacle. Do you feel resistant to doing this exercise, or are you excited about what it will bring to your life?

_____

_____

_____

_____

_____

_____

Claiming Your Power through Meditation

Any form of personal reflection can be considered meditation. Taking time in your day to witness and hold the circumstances of your life is an honor and privilege, though it does not feel that way when hurt, anger, and blame are in the forefront of your mind.

Exercise: Do you have a meditation practice of any sort in your life now? If so, describe it and what it brings to your life. If not, what are the resistances to starting a meditation practice?

_____

_____

_____

_____

_____

_____

Practices

THE INTRODUCTORY MEDITATION

This practice will give you the tools to turn your untrained mind into a mind of service. Be the observer, not the judge, in this practice and you will get a lot out of what you witness. Be gentle in your instruction to bring your mind back as it wanders off time and time again. Soon you will have an understanding of your task at hand, and the thoughtfulness of your meditation practice will stay with you throughout the day.

1 Come to your sacred space. Silence all phones and other devices and leave them in another room.

2 If the sensory experience is important to you, arrange the same conditions each time: the sheepskin mat or blanket underneath you, incense in the air, silence or neutral sounds such as moving water, sounds of air, or white noise playing in the background.

3 Set your meditation timer for three minutes.

4 Arrive with intention. This is good advice for any self-care practice but especially important for meditation. Arrive with purpose and release yourself to the moment. The opening of your practice is a beautiful time to connect with your higher self and the divine energy around you. I open all my practices by chanting "Ong Namo Guru Dev Namo" three times. This is known as the Adi mantra and is part of the Kundalini yoga tradition. It means "I bow to the subtle divine wisdom, I bow to the divine teacher within." However you decide to open your practice, come into starting position with your hands in prayer pose at your heart center and take a deep breath, centering yourself at the point between the brows. Through your breath, feel your connection to your higher self and to the energy that surrounds you. Stay here for six breaths.

5 Close your eyes and direct them to the point between the brows.

6 Once you have established the posture, begin Long Deep Breaths.

7 Hold your attention on the brow point and guide it back when it drifts away from that focus.

8   Breathe long and deep, and listen to the breath as it moves in and out of your body. Feel the sensations of the breath and hear the oceanic qualities of the sound and the warmth it brings to the back of your throat and chest.

9   Ideas, images, and distractions of all kinds will pop into your mind. When you notice that your attention has wandered, simply let the distraction go and bring your attention back to the brow point and the rhythm and sound of your breath. You may only have to guide your mind back once or twice, or possibly many, many times. Simply notice your focus. Don't judge it; just continually guide it back as you would a young child. Every day will be different. Do your best not to build a story around why it is different; simply allow the tides of your energy to flow in and out. If you need to analyze a situation that comes up more deeply, do this another time, not during your meditation practice.

10 Open your eyes when the timer sounds. At the closing of your practice, feel successful in all your efforts. Wrap your arms around yourself and celebrate your amazing courage.

11 Make notes in your journal of thoughts that came up and whether you want to further address them or simply let them go.

12 Close your practice by putting your hands together in prayer pose at your heart center, then take a deep healing breath and bow to your courage, your love of self, and your commitment to show up. I love reading the poem *Love After Love* by Derek Walcott when my practice is complete. It reminds me of how through my dedication to this practice, I come home again and again to myself!

13 Continue this practice for 40 days in a row. At the 20-day mark, increase your daily practice to six minutes.

AWARENESS IN WAKING UP

Start your day strong and purposefully. This day has so much potential; make the most of how you begin it. The morning hours are energetically charged and have the ability to support us through the day. Lay the foundation for your day through awareness, intention, and reflection.

1 Before you rise out of bed, give your body a stretch. Take a deep breath, and on the exhale, stretch your legs long, point your toes, and bring your arms overhead. Stretch, stretch, stretch.

2 Place your hands on your belly and do five rounds of the Long Deep Breath (inhale and exhale are one round).

3 Sit up on the side of the bed, and before you place your feet on the floor, take another couple of breaths.

4 Take a deep breath that brings in all the light and possibility of the day. On the exhale, release any concerns or worries, trusting that the universe will take care of them in the most perfect way.

5 Start your day!

chapter 10

The Heart

The energy of the heart filters through the mind, body, and spirit. This is its great value. When it is activated with awareness it has the power to bring compassion to our wounds, regrets, and losses and give us the chance to grow. Likewise, the heart energy flows through those parts already rich with offerings of love.

When we have been hurt deeply, it is hard to put ourselves in a vulnerable position again, but we have to do just that to find the promise of love again. Taking a look inside to see the sadness of the heart is the only way out of the pain. This is why self-care practices play such an important part in the healing of the heart. Otherwise the pain won't budge because it will feel far too big to deal with. It is likely the reason you didn't heal through your trauma the first time: the support systems were not in place for you to do that level of healing. This is not bad or good; it's just the reality of life. The wonderful news is that it can go right this time.

Facing Vulnerability

Taking a look inside to see the sadness of the heart is the only way out of pain. This is why self-care practices play such an important part in the healing of the heart. Otherwise the pain won't budge because it will feel too big to deal with. The wonderful news is that it can go right this time.

Exercise: Are you ready to look and listen to painful messages of the heart? Is there an event that happened in your early life (age 0–14) that made a painful impression on you? Please describe its affect on your heart.

_____

_____

_____

_____

_____

_____

Feeling the Effects of Love on the Four Elements

When we work to nurture our heart's love energy, we can heal beyond the fear that exists in life into a place where incredible things happen. Love's power is palpable. It is inclusive and compassionate and offers us understanding about ourselves and others. When we feel love at a physical level, we open and clear out things that hold us down. Love settles our minds and draws us to inward practices such as meditation and yoga. Love welcomes us inside ourselves with generous hospitality. It puts us in a higher way of being that unchains us from fear and suffering.

Exercise: Have you had an experience in your life where you have offered compassion to a difficult interaction with someone? Write about your experience. What did it feel like in your body, mind, heart, and spirit?

_____

_____

_____

_____

_____

_____

Practices

SELF SOOTHING

Over and over again we come around to the question "What does it take to make you feel safe?" Now is the time to get precise about the answer and fill up your self-care toolbox so you can reach for it in times of stress. These are some general ideas; the important thing is to find the tools that fit like a glove for you.

1 **Find your temperature.** This is a creature comfort that can be easily overlooked, but it is important. Know when your body needs to be warmed up or cooled off. For me, one of the most soothing things I can do is hold a hot water bottle to my chest before bed. (Mine is heart-shaped!)

2 **Find your comfort foods and drinks**. There are few things more classically comforting than a cup of warm tea. Food can be a touchy subject, as some of us are drawn to using food as a coping mechanism, but having a shortlist of nourishing whole foods that bring you comfort is a good thing.

3 **Gently stimulate your senses**. Give your senses somewhere gentle to rest. Choose soft fabrics to feel against your skin. Keep soothing photographs and artwork in the places you spend the most time. Have your favorite music ready on a streaming playlist or try a white noise machine.

4 **Nourish your heart with positive entertainment**. Our empathy is what makes us unique as a species. Soak up the emotional experiences of others through television shows and movies you connect with. Figure out if you are more soothed by humor, informative entertainment, drama, or something else.

WRITE A LETTER TO YOUR FUTURE SELF

Take some time in a quiet spot and compose a letter to yourself a year from now. Reflect on the circumstances of your life right now and any small moments of life that you'd like to reminisce about later. Then write down the aspirations you have for the future. How will daily life be different for future you? Which habits, relationships, and emotional cycles will be better? What will you be grateful for and have to celebrate? Give yourself advice and words of encouragement.

When you have finished your letter, seal it in an envelope and tuck it away somewhere safe, like the treasure box in your sacred space. Use a calendar app to set an appointment for a year in the future with a reminder of where you put the letter and a time to open it. For a low-tech alternate, entrust the letter to a very organized loved one to drop in the mail a year from now.

chapter 11

The Spirit

A strong and balanced spirit has the unique ability to trust the unknown, invisible, and intangible. Spirit is the ultimate believer. It can be more powerful in action than any other of the Four Elements of Human Life. When you depend upon spirit, it shows up and teaches you how to move out of fear and into faith. When we build a connection to spirit, we remember what it feels like to be in partnership. We access the knowledge of heaven and earth. Through relationship with the spirit, we have the chance to draw on knowledge that is otherwise not readily available to us.

Living at the mercy of your impulses is an ego-driven way of being that shuts out the wisdom of the spirit. The extreme highs and lows, competition, and backstabbing do not lay a foundation for the spirit to flourish. The joy of the spirit retreats. Instead, the spirit puts all its effort into waking you up. You start to feel suffering strongly. You overreact to the pain of uncertainty by rejecting responsibility, causing upheaval and hurting others. These warning signs are the spirit urging you to notice how uncomfortable and out of balance an ego-driven life is. And from that discomfort, you can take steps to change and align yourself with spirit once again.

Disconnecting from Spirit

Living at the mercy of your impulses is an ego-driven way of being that shuts out the wisdom of the spirit. Extreme highs and lows, competition, jealousy, and backstabbing do not lay a foundation for the spirit to flourish.

> **Exercise:** Have you fallen victim to the highs and lows of the ego? What was your experience and did you feel a disconnect from your spirit's energy?

_____

_____

_____

_____

_____

_____

Following the Spirit's Guidance

When we trust the spirit as a guide, we can let go of worry. The spirit's guidance is the most accurate directional system there is. The spirit is patient and constant, but there is no mistaking the power that the spirit holds.

Exercise: Have you ever had an experience where you have been able to let go of concern and let go completely? Describe the experience and what it felt like in all the elements of your life.

_____

_____

_____

_____

_____

_____

Practices

THE SENSITIVITY SCALE

Emotions are a function of the heart, but the intensity with which you feel them has a lot to do with the spirit. When dealing with the tough stuff in life, emotions can peak in intensity and can be difficult to deal with, which is why the numbness of apathy can be so appealing. But don't be afraid of strong emotions. They are an expression of a powerful spirit, and they function to ignite us into action.

This exercise is designed to help open us up to a stronger connection with the spirit. What's involved is simply to observe your engagement with your own emotions.

Throughout the day, name the emotion you are feeling, and on a scale of one to ten, rate how intense the feeling is for you or how engaged and present you feel, with one being the least and ten being the most. From there, ask yourself, "Am I okay with this level of engagement?" If it's a positive situation, what steps can you take to be more present? If it's a harmful situation, which of this book's self-care practices will help you to find strength again? The exercise prompts you to dialogue with your spirit and empowers you to move through situations. Keep asking questions, and the right answers will appear when you need them.

SPIRITUAL SAVINGS ACCOUNT

Think of your spirit as a bank account. The size and security of your bank account goes a long way to contributing to your life. The larger your bank account, the fewer your worries. You have your essentials covered, and you're even ready for an unforeseen large expense and withdrawal. Likewise, the smaller the bank account gets and the bigger the withdrawals, the more you are heading for trouble. When your bank account has reached its limit and goes into negative balance, it is a true emergency.

Now think of your spirit as the bank account, and your energy as the currency. When you make frequent deposits into your spiritual savings account through self-care, meditation, and other activities that bring you joy, you have plenty of currency in your account to handle the unexpected withdrawals from this energetic savings account. Pay attention to the quality and amount of energy you deposit into your spiritual savings account. Notice how much stronger life feels when there is abundant currency in the account.

What do deposits into the spiritual bank account look like? They can be anything we add to our lives to keep our perspective steady and give us the strength to flourish through all times. You are in charge of this energy, so get clear about what fills you up and what depletes you, continuously building on your energetic foundation so you can access what you need in challenging times.

Examples of spiritual savings account deposits:

* Eat wholesome, delicious, fresh foods

* Visit an art museum

* Go somewhere in your hometown that you've never visited before

* Wear your favorite color

* Make or buy an impromptu gift for someone you love

* Write a kind letter to someone you miss

* Join a club or volunteer group

* Go to the library or bookstore and pick out a book outside of your usual interests

* Spend time with the elderly at your local retirement home or senior center

* Volunteer for a few hours at your local animal shelter

* Make a recipe you've always wanted to try

I started using this practice in my life shortly after I started to meditate. Life began to feel more roomy very fast. I found myself less reactive and more capable of generosity in how I dealt with my own life. Instead of being filled to the brim with dread, sadness, and anger, my spiritual bank account was full and I was becoming a storehouse for positive, healing energy. Which simple pleasures would you like to put into your spiritual savings account?